Live Better relaxation

Live Better relaxation

exercises and inspirations for well-being

Dr Sarah Brewer

BARNES & NOBLE BOOKS

BOOKS

NEW YORK

Live Better: Relaxation

Sarah Brewer

This edition published by Barnes & Noble, Inc.
by arrangement with Duncan Baird Publishers

2003 Barnes & Noble

M 10 9 8 7 6 5 4 3 2 1

ISBN: 0-7607-4920-5

Conceived, created and designed by
Duncan Baird Publishers Ltd
Sixth Floor , Castle House
75–76 Wells Street
London W1T 3QH

Managing Editors: Judy Barratt
Editor: Louise Nixon
Managing Designer: Manisha Patel
Designer: Allan Sommerville
Picture Research: Cecilia Weston-Baker

Library of congress Cataloging-in-Publication
Data is available.

Typeset in Filosofia and Son Kern
Colour reproduction by Scanhouse, Malaysia
Printed and bound in Thailand by Sirivatana
Interprint (SI)

PUBLISHER'S NOTE

Before following any advice or practice
suggested in this book, it is recommended
that you consult your doctor as to its
suitability, especially if you suffer from
any health problems or special conditions.
The publishers, author and photographers
cannot accept any responsibility for any
injuries or damage incurred as a result of
following the exercises in this book, or of
using any of the relaxation techniques
described or mentioned here.

contents

INTRODUCTION

As a GP and hospital doctor, I have seen hundreds of people whose health and quality of life are adversely affected by excess stress. I have held seminars on coping with stress for pressurized executives and doctors alike. However, over the years, I have also seen how relaxation techniques, incorporated easily into people's lives, have helped to ease their everyday burdens so that they may live more happily and more healthily.

Oddly, I often find that when they are completely stressed out, people think of anything but taking time out specifically for relaxation. I often hear the rationale that there are far too many more "important" things to do. However, with a little gentle persuasion, even the busiest people soon realize that short periods of relaxation have a hugely positive impact on their health and well-being. At first these periods of de-stressing provide "fix-it" time to help correct the impact of built-up stress. Ultimately, however, they become a regular part of keeping stress at bay.

As you have probably already experienced, having some pressure in your life is essential to help you achieve your personal best: a certain level of pressure helps to generate the ambition and drive to get things done. However, too much pressure may cause physical and emotional syptoms summed up in the word "distress". Conversely, if you are only operating in your "comfort zone", it is unlikely that your skills are being used to the full. This may result in a lack of stimulation, boredom and even a lack of purpose or meaning in life.

This book is designed to help you build relaxation into your life, so that you can reap the advantages of positive pressure without succumbing to the harmful effects of negative pressure, or stress. You will find nuggets of wisdom and quotations interspersed throughout the book, which will inspire you on your journey. There are also many different kinds of exercises to try, aimed at relaxing both mind and body. Create an individual approach to relaxation by choosing the exercises that appeal to you most. Schedule time do them. Start with two or three a week, and build up gradually to one a day.

Chapter One

reclaiming relaxation

Relaxation, a state in which we experience a calm mind and a body free from tension, is essential for our health and well-being. The trouble is that in modern life stress seems to be the normal state of existence. While a certain amount of stress is important to help us rise to life's challenges, too much for too long may lead to symptoms of ill-health. In order to reclaim relaxation as our rightful way to live, we need first to identify why stress has taken hold.

Most people can readily recognize when they are under stress. As well as the physical symptoms (a racing pulse, increased sweating, muscle tension, and so on), you may also experience emotional problems, such as anxiety and a sense of hopelessness. You may also notice behavioural changes, such as aggression or an increased reliance on cigarettes or alcohol.

The exercises given in this book are effective for countering all the various effects of stress. In this chapter we discover the need for relaxation in our lives. We explore what stress is and how the stress response impacts our body and mind. We learn how to pinpoint the causes of stress in our daily life. Finally, we take our first steps to relaiming relaxation by monitoring our stress response and doing simple relaxation exercises, as well as opening our understanding to Eastern concepts of energy flow.

THE NEED FOR RELAXATION

Focused relaxation is vital for prolonged well-being – it helps to counterbalance the negative effects of stress on our mental and physical health. When we make a conscious effort to relax, through techniques such as meditation, visualization, massage and even exercise, we encourage the mind to become calm (by emptying it of troublesome thoughts) and the body to become loose. Many physiological benefits result from relaxation, ranging from lowered blood pressure and reduced arteriosclerosis (thickening of arterial walls) to slower brain-cell deterioration and age-related memory loss.

When the body winds down from a high-stress situation, our inbuilt safety mechanism, the "fight-or-flight" reaction (see pages 13–15) is switched off and an opposite reaction occurs, known as the "rest-and-digest" response. You can consciously switch off your stress response through breathing and relaxation exercises so that your breathing and heartbeat slow down and your muscle tension lessens.

THE STRESS FACTOR

What is stress?

In modern times the term stress is commonly used negatively to describe a state in which we experience greater pressure than we can cope with – physically, mentally or emotionally. Although it may sound strange, there is an optimum level of pressure for each of us. The amount of stress on our bodies and minds caused by this optimum acts in a positive way, making us feel challenged, excited and motivated. However, when we move past this optimum level, we begin to experience certain unpleasant physical, emotional and behavioural symptoms. These indicate that something is wrong. Many of these symptoms are associated with ill-health and may occur separately or in combination. One set of symptoms may even trigger another. Headaches, lack of energy, sleeplessness, tension in the body, over- or undereating, and feelings of sadness or depression, and extreme emotions such as anger or frustration, are all symptoms of over-stress or *distress*.

There is no universal level of pressure at which distress kicks in. Different people are comfortable with different amounts of pressure; our ability to cope varies from person to person and even from time to time. Studies even show that most stress is self-generated — unfounded feelings of insecurity give rise to a sense of being unable to cope with or adapt to changes occurring at work or at home. The good news is that if we can create distress, then we can certainly uncreate it, too!

"Fight or flight" – the physical reaction

The body responds to distress in a number of ways. The most basic of these is the "fight-or-flight" reaction, and it was crucial for the survival of primitive humans. This physical response owes mostly to the effects on the body of adrenaline (epinephrine), a hormone produced in the adrenal glands. During periods of heightened stress, in only one minute levels of adrenaline in the blood can increase as much as a thousandfold. Adrenaline can have a number of effects on the body, including some or all of the following examples:

- The heart contracts faster and harder, raising your pulse rate and blood pressure, and sending more blood to your brain and muscles. This makes you more alert and reactive to danger.
- Blood sugar levels increase to provide an energy boost for the muscles.
- The sweat glands increase sweat production ready to cool you down during sudden exercise.
- The muscles become tense and ready for action, and you may start to shake.
- You begin to breathe more rapidly in order to bring extra oxygen into the body.
- Your pupils dilate to increase your field of vision.
- Your intestines empty (through nervous diarrhea or vomiting) to make you lighter for running.
- Chemicals are released into the blood that help clot it more easily and cause damaged blood vessels to constrict, reducing the amount of bleeding from any cuts and wounds sustained.

As the above makes clear, during the first stage of the stress reaction energy is mobilized within the body (it is then consumed and drained). This response was vital for primitive humans, who needed the changes to help prepare the body for action against enemies or dangerous animals. For our ancestors the vigorous exercise involved in the fight-or-flight response helped consume the surge of energy, thus neutralizing the effects of adrenaline and restoring the body systems to a state of equilibrium (known as homeostasis). But in modern times we rarely need to fight or flee – we tend to experience stress under less energetic conditions (think how pent up you become during a traffic jam or a difficult negotiation with a client). Consequently stress is not "burnt off" and its effects build up in our bodies, which can lead to long-term health problems.

Overcoming stress

Finding our optimum level of pressure or tension is like adjusting the strings of a musical instrument: too loose and the sound is ruined; too tight and the strings will break. However, when we get the tension just right the strings work in harmony to produce a perfect sound.

A MOMENT FOR MYSELF

Try to find time to relax at least once a day.
Pick the same time each day if you can, so that
relaxation becomes a natural part of your routine.
Let people know not to call or visit you at this time.
Find somewhere warm, comfortable and quiet to sit
and contemplate. Play a cassette or CD of repetitive
sounds (such as the sound of the sea or the wind) and
light an incense stick to help create a mood
of tranquillity. You might practise one of the
meditations or visualizations in this book, or
you might simply sit quietly and empty your
mind of the events of the day.

IDENTIFYING THE TRIGGERS

Keeping a stress diary, even for only a week, will help you pinpoint the main causes of distress in your life, and help you monitor the negative responses (physical, emotional and behavioural) they trigger.

For each day of the week, divide a page in a notebook into five columns and label them with the following headings (as shown on the opposite page): Time, Situation, Feelings, Negative Responses and Corrective Actions. Carry the notebook round with you and try to make a note of a stressful occurrence immediately after the event (rather than relying on your memory). Record your feelings as accurately as possible and try to identify a simple corrective action straight away.

At the end of the week, analyze your journal to identify your most common stress triggers. Ask yourself these questions: which situations caused you the most stress? Were your responses appropriate, and if not how could you have reacted in a more constructive way? Make a conscious effort to implement your corrective actions.

MONDAY

Time	Situation	Feelings	Negative Responses	Corrective Actions
8.25	Stuck in traffic.	Worried that will be late for work.	Shouted at other drivers for being slow.	Play soothing music in the car.
8.45	Missed train.	Annoyed and irritable.	Bought a donut for breakfast.	Get up in time to have healthy breakfast.
9.45	Computer crashes.	Frustrated that can't get on with work.	Complain to everyone at work about computer system.	Speak calmly to person responsible for fixing computer.
12.30	Unpleasant 'phone call from irate customer.	Upset, angry. Not my fault the delivery was delayed.	Had two glasses of wine with lunch and moaned to colleagues.	Go for a run at lunchtime to burn off stress hormones and keep fit.
18.00	Shopping in crowded grocery store.	Frustrated, irritable, angry.	Went home without several items. Bought comfort snacks.	Sign on for internet ordering and delivery from store.

READING THE SIGNS

Some of the first signs that we are under too much pressure may be so mild that they simply go unnoticed – clenched teeth is just one example of such a physical symptom. Other symptoms may be emotional or behavioural. Learning to recognize your own telltale signs is one of the most important keys to reclaiming relaxation.

Physical symptoms

Look out for periods of increased sweating or flushing, a racing pulse, trembling, nausea and nervous diarrhea. When the stress response is prolonged, you may also develop palpitations, dizziness, faintness and numbness or pins and needles. Some of these symptoms are a result of overbreathing (hyperventilation). Prolonged exposure to excess stress can lead to tension headaches, migraines, insomnia, exhaustion and bad dreams. You may be more prone to recurrent infections, such as coughs, colds, lip sores, and thrush. Look out for areas of muscle tension, especially in the shoulders and neck.

Emotional symptoms

Be aware of overwhelming feelings of anxiety and sometimes panic (in severe cases these can lead to panic
attacks). You may find it difficult to concentrate or make
decisions; you may overwork through a fear of failure; or
you may feel complete helplessness. Another emotional
symptom is a loss of sex drive.

Behavioural symptoms

People under excess stress often change their behaviour. For example, some people may develop an over-
reliance on alcohol, cigarettes or drugs (whether
prescribed or illegal). Others may simply change from
being generally calm and placid to irrational or irritable.
Obsessive or compulsive behaviour, such as over- or
undereating, are also common symptoms. Some people
become aggressive, while others may go out of their way
to avoid certain places, situations or people.

If you are experiencing any of the above symptoms, it's
time to help put your body and mind back into balance.

RELEASING YOUR STRESS

Many of us "internalize" during times of
stress, but bottling things up is one of the worst
things we can do, as it causes a volatile build-up of
negative emotions that may explode at any time. Make
a conscious effort to release stress regularly. At the end
of each day, reflect on aspects of the day that made you
anxious. As you bring each situation to mind, try to
view it dispassionately. Then breathe out and
imagine that with your out-breath you offer the
issue up to the Universe, releasing it and
freeing yourself from its burden.

RELAXING VISUALIZATION

Visualization provides an effective escape from the stress of everyday life. In this visualization you create an idyllic retreat to which you can escape at any time. The first time you practise this visualization, be diligent about noting every detail – that way you will be able to recreate your haven quickly at future times of stress.

1 Sit comfortably and close your eyes. Retreat in your mind to a small desert island with golden sand, turquoise sea and lush, tropical foliage.

2 Use all of your senses to explore this imaginary world: feel the warm sun on your skin, the soft sand beneath your feet and a gentle breeze blowing through your hair. Revel in the vibrant flashes of red, yellow and orange in birds and flowers; smell the scent of jasmine or the salty scent of the sea. What sounds can you hear?

3 Delight in this scene until you feel calm. When you feel ready, gently bring your awareness back to the present.

THE BALANCE OF QI

According to some Eastern philosophies, health and well-being depend on the balance of an invisible vital energy in the body, known as *qi* or *ch'i* in China and as *ki* in Japan. When a person is healthy, *qi* flows smoothly along channels in the body known as meridians. The flow of *qi* depends on the balance of two complementary yet opposing forces: yin and yang. When yin and yang are imbalanced in the body (from stress, poor diet or spiritual neglect), energy flow through the meridians becomes blocked and causes the symptoms of illness.

Many of the Eastern exercise and medical disciplines (among them acupuncture, acupressure, shiatsu and t'ai chi) focus on the act of rebalancing yin and yang in order to harmonize the flow of *qi* in the body.

The idea that reclaiming relaxation is an act of rebalancing energy within the body can provide a useful tool in meditations and visualizations, and an important rule of thumb for living. Try to keep it in mind throughout your relaxation journey.

If I keep a green bough in my heart, the
singing bird will come.

CHINESE PROVERB

Qi is within each of us. Heaven
and earth and every living thing require *qi* to
stay alive. Those who know how to allow their
qi to circulate will preserve themselves and
banish illnesses.

KO HUNG

(*c.*281–*c.*341)

Chapter Two

mind-body harmony

As we already know, stress is built up in the body (our muscles tense, our breathing becomes shallow and irregular and often we experience forms of physical discomfort, such as headaches or extreme tiredness). It makes sense, then, that the first step on our road to relaxation should be to use physical methods to bring our body and mind back into a state of balance.

Relaxation is a holistic process. When we nourish our physical self, we nourish our mental self, too. In this chapter we explore the various ways by which we can ease our body and in the process ease our mind. We look at precise physical techniques, such as yoga (which aims to bring the mind and body into balance

through posture, breath awareness and meditation)
and special breathing exercises (which aim to remind
us how calming it feels to breathe deeply and regularly). We also discover how deep muscle-relaxation
exercises can help release built-up tension that,
unchecked, can lead to aches, pains and stiffness in
muscles and joints. We learn how a heightened appre-
ciation of our senses can prove invaluable for a more
peaceful state of mind. For example, through some
forms of touch our body can release its natural
painkillers or balance our *qi* energy; while sound
therapy can help to slow our brainwaves to induce a
profound sense of relaxation.

YOGA

An excellent way to develop balance in mind and body is through the practice of yoga. One of India's philosophical traditions, yoga originated in the Indus Valley (in modern Pakistan) and dates back almost three thousand years. In the West yoga has become increasingly popular in recent years, owing to well-documented evidence about its benefits. There are eight "branches" of yoga in total and each branch has the same ultimate aim – that of self-realization through the union of body and mind.

Hatha yoga is an umbrella term for the branch of yoga that concentrates on posture and it is the most widely practised branch of yoga in the West. Performing physical postures or *asana*s releases muscle tension and increases suppleness, as well as calming the mind. As with all therapies, it is best to receive training from a qualified teacher who will help you achieve the right yoga positions for you. Breathing constitutes a major element of yoga practice, and plays an important role in bringing emotional and mental harmony.

MEDITATION

Meditation is a discipline that uses the power of the mind to control thoughts, calm the body and achieve a state of heightened mental or spiritual awareness. By focusing your mind on a particular object (such as a candle flame), a vision or a sound, or even by turning it inward to stillness, you screen out distractions and learn to access more fully your "inner core". Those experienced in meditation can enter a trance-like state in which the brain generates a type of brainwave known as the theta wave, associated with profound relaxation.

One of the most common focuses for meditation is sound. Some people use traditional mantras, such as "om", but using a word or phrase with personal meaning (known as an affirmation) can be just as effective. Try meditating on the phrase "I am peace." Many of the exercises in this chapter feature techniques that can help you achieve a meditative state, among them visualization (see page 37), in which a scene is conjured up in the mind's eye, and breath awareness (see page 43).

If you detach yourself from identification with the body
and remain relaxed in and as Consciousness, you will,
this very moment, be happy and at peace.

ASHTAVAKRA GITA (8TH CENTURY)

Give your thoughts a chance to settle down. Then feel
your mind clear like a still forest pool.

THE BUDDHA

(c.563–c.483BCE)

CALMING VISUALIZATION

In this visualization you engage your senses to explore the colours, sounds and smells of a beautiful garden. Use it whenever you need to induce a sense of calm.

1 Sit comfortably in a quiet place with subdued lighting. Close your eyes and imagine your favourite colour — allow this colour to cover your whole field of vision.

2 Now visualize a garden filled with plants and flowers — splashes of green are interspersed with yellow, orange, red, pink and white. Wisps of cloud float in a blue sky and golden sunlight filters down through the trees.

3 Bring in your senses of smell and hearing. You can detect the scent of roses and honeysuckle in the air. In the background you hear the buzz of insects and the wind rustling in the leaves, while birds chirrup and sing. Tune into these scents and sounds for a moment as you drift into a relaxed, meditative state.

4 When you feel ready to do so, let the image of the garden slowly fade from your mind and gently open your eyes.

THE INNER SMILE

The next time you notice yourself feeling tense or
stressed, try the technique of the "inner smile". In
ancient Chinese medicine a similar approach to this is
said to activate the *tan tien*, the energy store of your
body, just below your navel. Think of something that
makes you feel happy: this could be the smell of freshly
baked bread or a joyful moment from your past —
anything that makes you smile inwardly. Allow this
smile to travel within you until it sits in your abdomen
radiating warmth throughout your body.

LEARNING TO BREATHE

There are close links between your state of mind and the way you breathe – the ancient yogis established this fact many thousands of years ago. For most of the time, most people use only a third of their maximum lung capacity to take in air. Often this is simply through bad habit; sometimes it is a direct result of stress.

When you are in a state of relaxation, your breathing should be slow, deep and regular. During times of stress your breathing becomes fast, shallow and irregular – you may sigh deeply, gasp and even hold your breath. At such times the typical breathing rate increases from an average of ten to approximately twenty breaths per minute. When feeling over-anxious or panicky, some people's breathing rate can even increase to as much as thirty breaths per minute. Overbreathing (otherwise known as hyperventilation) affects the way in which oxygen and carbon dioxide enter and leave the body, causing an imbalance in the ratio of these gases within you. This may cause further symptoms, such as chest pain, muscle spasm and, if hyperventilation persists for a long time, even total collapse. In fact, hyperventilation is now recognized as one of the main triggers of panic attacks.

Breathing practice forms an integral part of Eastern relaxation practices, such as yoga and meditation. In yoga the breath is thought to embody the life force or *prana* (a similar concept to Chinese *qi*; see page 26). Breathing exercise, known as *pranayama*, is believed to bring mental and emotional harmony by linking the breath with the body and mind.

Observation of how we breathe is crucial for relaxation to occur. Practise breathing calmly, slowly and deeply from the diaphragm. To help you do this, place your hand on your abdomen and feel it rise as your diaphragm and lungs expand (in shallow breathing it is the chest that expands). You could also try visualizing a candle flame in front of you – imagine that it merely flickers gently as you slowly breathe in and out. Make sure you keep your stomach and shoulder muscles relaxed (see page 49), as tension here will interfere with deep, relaxed breathing.

THE COMPLETE BREATH

Yogic breath control or *pranayama* is said to influence the flow of *prana* in the body to promote good health, as well as longevity and even spiritual enlightenment. This *pranayama* exercise is known as the "complete breath".

1 Remove your shoes, loosen your clothing and lie down on the floor with your eyes closed and your arms relaxed by your sides. Breathe in slowly through your nose and visualize your lungs expanding and filling with air as you do so. When you have reached your maximum lung capacity, hold your breath for a moment before exhaling slowly (through your nose) to empty your lungs fully.

2 On the next in-breath keep the inhalation short (two to three seconds) then gradually increase the length of every exhalation until it takes seven to eight seconds.

3 Concentrate on keeping the air movement slow and continuous (don't breathe out quickly and then hold your breath for the end of the count before breathing in again). Continue for as long as you feel comfortable.

When the breath is irregular, the mind is also unsteady,
but when the breath is still, so is the mind.

HATHAYOGAPRADIPIKA (14TH CENTURY)

Pranayama [breath control] is the regulation of the
inhalation, exhalation and suspension of the breath.
By observing the length and duration of these phases,
you can make the breath long and subtle.

PATANJALI

YOGA SUTRAS (c.200BCE–c.200CE)

BREATHE INTO CALM

You can feel instantly more calm simply by bringing
your awareness to your breath. If you are
in a situation that is giving rise to panic, focus on your
breath for a moment. As you breathe in, push out your
abdomen as though you were blowing up a balloon in
your stomach, moving your chest as little as possible.
As you breathe out consciously drop your shoulders and
squeeze all the air out of your abdomen as though
you were squeezing water out of a sponge. Do this
for two complete breaths.

HAND AND LEG SHAKES

This is an excellent tension-busting exercise,
which you can perform almost anywhere. Shake your
hands and arms for one minute and then your legs and
feet. When you stop shaking them, your muscles should
feel completely soft and relaxed.

SHOULDER AND NECK RELAXER

We often carry tension in our shoulders and neck.
With your arms by your sides, imagine you are carrying
a heavy weight in each hand so that your shoulders are
pulled toward the floor. Hold for five seconds. Now
imagine dropping the weights to the floor and feeling
the tension release. Repeat this sequence five times.

WHOLE BODY RELAXATION

The following deep-relaxation exercise will help you relieve tension in all parts of your body. Keep your eyes closed and breathe gently and slowly throughout.

1 Lie down in a warm, quiet place. Lift your forearms and clench your fists tight for a moment. As you breathe out let the tension drain away, then release your clenched fists and lower your arms to your sides.

2 Shrug your shoulders as high as you can. Hold for a moment, then release.

3 Tighten your facial muscles by clenching your teeth, frowning, and screwing up your eyes. Hold, then let go.

4 In turn tense and release the muscles in your back, abdomen, buttocks, legs and feet. After you have done this, your whole body should feel heavy − imagine it sinking happily into the floor. Get up slowly once you feel totally relaxed.

THE CALMING TOUCH

Touch is a simple way to express affection and reassurance to another person and most people find it immediately calming (experiencing the soothing qualities of touch is vital for babies to thrive). It is perhaps because touch is so soothing that massage is one of the oldest and most widely practised therapies in the world. In addition, techniques such as acupressure, shiatsu and reflexology draw upon touch as a therapeutic resource.

Massage

Unexpressed emotions are believed to build up in the nervous system, causing muscle tension. By releasing the tension, massage frees the emotions to rebalance the mind, body and spirit and induce a sense of profound relaxation, strengthen the immune system and improve our general health. The combination of different strokes used in massage (such as kneading, drumming, friction strokes and effleurage) also eases circulatory problems and high blood pressure, and has a positive effect on physiological disturbances that can cause anxiety, lower the mood and induce poor-quality sleep. Massage also stimulates the release of the body's natural painkillers (known as endorphins) and these relieve physical discomfort. Try the massage exercise on page 57. The technique may also be combined with relaxing aromatherapy oils (see pages 66–7).

Acupressure

An ancient technique, which has been practised in China and Japan for more than three thousand years, acupressure uses thumb pressure or fingertip massage to relax areas of tension and free the flow of *qi* (the life force) in the body. One of the best-known examples of acupressure is shiatsu (in Japanese the word means "finger pressure"). In a shiatsu session, practitioners may also use their forearms and elbows, and sometimes even their knees or feet, as well as their fingers, thumbs and palms, to stimulate pressure points on the skin. The following pages give examples of acupressure that can be self-applied at times of stress.

SELF-HELP ACUPRESSURE

Although acupressure is usually applied by a practitioner on a patient, there are some simple techniques that can be self-practised. When you do the following exercises, apply an even pressure. Try to keep your body relaxed and your breathing regular throughout the acupressure session. You may experience a slight tingling sensation in the area you are massaging − release the pressure if it becomes painful.

Stimulate awareness

The acupoint located in the fleshy part of the hand between the thumb and forefinger (close to where the bones meet), helps stimulate mental awareness of the world around us. Hold your left hand, palm down, in front of you, supporting it with the fingers of your right hand. Spread your thumb and forefinger. With your right thumb apply firm downward pressure on the acupoint. Hold for about two minutes, then swap hands. (Do not stimulate this acupoint during pregnancy.)

Clear your mind

Using one of your index fingers, identify the point between your eyebrows in the middle of your forehead. Apply firm pressure here while making small rotations both clockwise and anticlockwise over the point. Continue for three minutes or so.

Boost vitality

The acupoint located just below the ball of your foot, a third of the way along the sole, is used to boost vitality and relieve fatigue. Sit with your right foot on your left knee. Apply pressure to the acupoint with your right thumb for two minutes. Repeat on your left foot.

Improve concentration

Concentration is one of the first mental processes to suffer under stress. When treated, the acupoint located in the groove above the upper lip improves mental alert- ness and memory. Gently apply pressure (perpendicular to the groove) with the tip of your index finger or the edge of its fingernail (of either hand) for three minutes.

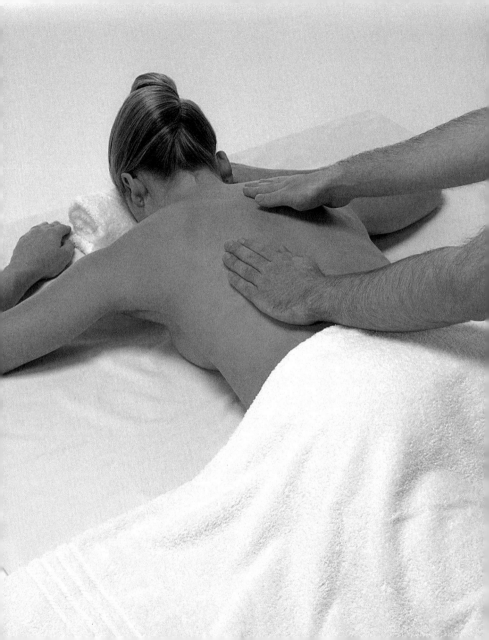

GENTLE MASSAGE

Take turns with a partner to give and receive a massage. This will help ease tension, improve circulation and promote a sense of connectedness between you both.

1 Ask your partner to lie face down on a towel. Warm some massage oil by rubbing it into your hands.

2 Place the heels of your hands on either side at the base of your partner's spine, fingertips curling round their waist. Make long strokes up toward their shoulders, keeping one hand in contact with their body at all times.

3 Vary the pressure and length of the strokes, keeping your movements rhythmic and gentle. When you have finished massaging the back of the body (including the backs of the legs and arms), ask your partner to turn over. Begin in the same way — with the torso, before moving to the limbs. Always work toward the heart.

4 To finish hold your partner's feet for a few seconds, as this helps to "ground" them. Now it's your turn.

EATING, SLEEPING, BEING

People often think that stress and relaxation are
things that happen only in the mind. In fact any
negative influences on the body can cause distress.
One way to keep these to a minimum is to eat a healthy,
preferably organic diet and keep your intake of salt,
caffeine, alcohol and food additives to a minimum.
If you smoke do your utmost to stop. Finally, don't
push your body too hard – obtain adequate amounts
of sleep (between six and eight hours a night).

There is no feeling, except the extremes of fear and
grief, that does not find relief in music.

GEORGE ELIOT

(1819–90)

Music produces a kind of pleasure that human
nature cannot do without.

CONFUCIUS

(c.551–c.479 BCE)

SOUNDS OF PEACE

Among the most accessible aids to relaxation are the sounds of nature. Think how calming it is to lie in an open field with only the birdsong and breeze to listen to. If you live in the countryside, you have the potential for relaxtion on your doorstep. Take some time out to enjoy it! If you live in a city or town, try buying a CD or cassette of nature's sounds. There are many recordings available — I recommend the sounds of a brook, the lapping waves of the sea, the rainforest at twilight or the calls of dolphins and whales.

Play the sounds before falling asleep, or to add a further dimension to a visualization or relaxation exercise. If there is a rhythm (as there might be with waves), try to attune your breathing to it. For a really sublime experience, run an aromatherapy bath (see page 68), light a few candles and lie in the soothing water while listening to your recording. (Do not use electrical equipment in the bathroom — position speakers just outside the door, or use a battery-powered player.)

YOUR OWN SOUNDS OF CALM

In this exercise you record your own personalized relaxation cassette. The idea is to choose a selection of songs or sounds that you find particularly soothing.

1   Set aside enough time to record 30 minutes of listening time. Go through your music collection and pick out tracks that you know you find calming, such as classical pieces, or slow songs that remind you of happy times.

2   If you have a quiet area of natural beauty near by, try recording some sounds of nature, such as running water or birdsong. When you are happy with your recording, try it out. Prepare a warm room with candles. Set the cassette to play and lie comfortably on your back. Allow your breathing to become regular and soft.

3   During the musical pieces try to distinguish the instruments from one another; focus on the "spaces" in the music as well as the sounds. During the sounds of nature, try to recapture the relevant scene and allow the sounds to fill your consciousness.

SOOTHING AROMATHERAPY

The potency of smell has been used to stimulate the senses for more than four thousand years. Aromatherapy (known to have been practised in ancient India, Egypt, Greece and Rome) is the art of using essential oils, derived from plants, for their beneficial effects on health and their soothing, relaxant properties. Oils may be diluted and massaged into the skin, added to bath water (see page 68) or heated in specially devised burners to perfume the air.

Each essential oil has its own characteristic aroma and profile of therapeutic properties. Some oils are stimulating and invigorating, while others are calming and soothing. The following aromatherapy oils are known to be especially helpful for relaxation: geranium, grapefruit, jasmine, lavender, lemongrass, neroli, orange, rose, rosewood, sandalwood, vanilla, vetiver and ylang ylang. Select one oil that appeals to you, or if you prefer blend two or three together until you obtain an overall scent that you like.

As far as possible use natural rather than synthetic essential oils, as they have a fuller, sweeter aroma and a greater therapeutic effect. Those described as "100 per cent pure" are more expensive but preferable, as they have not been mixed with alcohol or other additives.

To create a relaxing atmosphere, use two to three drops of oil in a vaporizer or oil-burner (increase the number of drops of oil if the room is large). Make sure that you place the burner in a safe place (especially out of the reach of children and pets).

If you are using essential oils in a massage, be aware that they are highly concentrated and should be diluted with a carrier oil before they come into contact with the skin. Carrier oils you could use include almond, avocado, sunflower and wheatgerm oils.

Pure essential oils can be harmful if used in excess, so always choose oils carefully and follow the instructions that come with the pack. Do not use them if you have a medical problem or are pregnant, except under the guidance of a qualified aromatherapist. Discontinue use if you develop a skin irritation or allergic reaction.

AN AROMATIC BATH

Aromatherapy is wonderfully relaxing when used in the bath. The therapeutic properties of the oils are absorbed into the skin, as well as being inhaled via the breath.

1   Choose a single favourite sensuous oil, or a blend of up to three. Add five drops of essential oil to a tablespoon (30 ml) of carrier oil (see page 67) and mix. Draw the bath so that it is comfortably hot, then pour the aromatic oil mix into the bathwater. (Don't add the oil until you have stopped running the water.)

2   Close the bathroom door to keep in the vapours, and get into the bath. Lie back comfortably and close your eyes. Allow the scent to fill your entire body. Imagine it coursing through your veins, bringing relaxation and a renewed sense of energy.

3   Soak for 15 to 20 minutes, preferably in candlelight. When you feel ready, slowly get out of the bath.

RESTORATIVE SLEEP

We each spend a third of our life asleep. A form of unconsciousness that is our natural state of rest, sleep is a period of rejuvenation and regeneration that is essential for our physical and mental health. During sleep muscles and joints recover from constant use during the day, and our body increases production of new cells — most of the body's repair work occurs while we are asleep. Surprisingly, studies show that most of the brain is just as active during sleep as when we are wide awake. This activity may relate to dreaming, which also seems to be essential for health.

To help you sleep well, avoid overindulgence in substances that interfere with sleep, such as caffeine (found in coffee, tea, chocolate, colas), nicotine and alcohol. Take time to unwind from the stresses of the day before going to bed — read a book, listen to soothing music or use aromatherapy oils in the bath (see page 68). Get into the habit of going to bed at a regular time each night and getting up at the same time each morning.

STRATEGIES FOR SLEEPING WELL

Make sure your bed is comfortable, and your
bedroom is dark and quiet. Keep the room warm
— a temperature of 18 to 24°C (64 to 75°F) is ideal.
Place a few drops of relaxing lavender essential oil
on a handkerchief and tuck it near your pillow. If you
can't fall asleep, get up and read, listen to the radio, or
watch the television for a while. If you find yourself
worrying about something, write down all the things on
your mind and promise yourself you will deal with
them in the morning. Then go back to bed.

Chapter Three

the inner realm

To achieve full relaxation it is vital to be at peace with ourselves and our emotions; the psychological aspects of relaxation are just as crucial as being able to release tension from the physical body. Maintaining a well-developed sense of personal identity helps us have a balanced perspective on life and a vital, healthy belief in ourselves. If we believe in ourselves, we can work through any of life's difficulties – in fact, we may even grasp stressful situations as opportunities for personal growth and increased self-awareness.

In order to realize your full potential, you need to learn to recognize and respect your good points, and use others' feedback to work on your shortcomings, turning them into strengths rather than weaknesses. You can learn to achieve a balanced perspective on yourself by encouraging positive self-talk, rather than engaging in damaging self-criticism.

Certain visualizations may help you to believe that you are good enough; others may help you identify what you desire from life. When we create a detailed mental vision of something, that something becomes more real for us, and more attainable.

In this chapter we look at techniques for exploring our inner realm. By practising them regularly we can increase our self-esteem, discover our goals, let go of our past and create a bright vision of the future.

VALUING YOURSELF

If you do not believe in yourself and you find no value in your individual qualities, you will find it increasingly difficult to relax. As we have already seen, stress arises when the pressure of commitments and responsibilities exceeds the boundaries within which you feel you can cope. If you have a good sense of self-worth and a strong sense of your abilities, these boundaries will be broad. You can then look on pressure in a positive way – as a chance to expand your experience and skills.

You can develop a good sense of self by learning to recognize and respect your good points. Make a list of them and be sure to include things that appear mundane at first glance (for example, being punctual). Perhaps you have a natural ability to empathize, a bubbly sense of humour, or a willingness to help others. Think about all these good points whenever you lack self-esteem. Furthermore, you should learn to accept praise and be glad when you have done well. The next time someone compliments you, smile and say thank you. Whatever you do, try not to laugh off praise – you deserve every bit of it, so relish the moment!

All too often we allow our self-belief to be undermined by the criticism of others. However, no one can make you feel inferior without your permission – they can only invite you to. How you react to any criticism is your decision. The next time someone makes you feel inferior, say to yourself: "I believe in myself, and that is all that matters." Then assess whether the criticism is valid. If it is you can agree openly to take the comment on board (recognizing the self-improvement you are making as you do so). But if it is unfair, be assertive. Say that you disagree and explain why. Try not to sound defensive, but reasoned. Even when you agree, criticism can be hurtful. Keep reminding yourself of your statement: "I believe in myself, and that is all that matters."

Make plans to learn something new about yourself each week, by improving your skills or gaining wider experiences in life. And finally, never think that you aren't good enough – you *are* good enough and should tell yourself so every day.

REGAIN PERSPECTIVE

If the same problem keeps coming to the fore and you can think of no new ways to deal with it, try this visualization exercise to put it into perspective and let it go.

1   Sit comfortably, take a few deep breaths and close your eyes. In your mind's eye imagine that you are a bird taking flight. You sweep up into the sky, soaring high above your human self.

2   Look down. What can you see? From the air explore the houses, buildings and streets. People appear as tiny dots, moving hurriedly from place to place.

3   Fly higher still. Buildings and trees appear to shrink away. Eventually all you can see beneath you is the world as a small, revolving ball hovering in space.

4   From here try to visualize your problem as a speck of dust on the Earth below you. Think how the wind will pick it up and blow it far away. When you feel ready to do so, slowly breathe out, then open your eyes.

CONQUERING FEAR

For some of us, overcoming fear is one of the most significant keys to living a more relaxed life. Fear, by its very nature, is an inner realm — an emotion conjured up within us in response to perceived danger. Sometimes that danger is real, but often it is imagined. Whether you fear public speaking or "the future", heights or spiders, fear is extremely stressful, but it can be conquered.

One of the best ways to control irrational fear is through a slow process of desensitization. Build up your tolerance one step at a time. For example, if you are terrified of giving speeches, offer a short toast at a small family gathering. See how much everyone enjoys your gesture and take courage from it. The next time, make a brief speech, or give a vote of thanks to the host or cook. Before long presenting to a group of delegates will simply be another step on the ladder — and not nearly as daunting as it once was. Another approach is to visualize yourself overcoming your fear in as much detail as possible. Then conquer it for real.

Do the thing you fear the most and the death
of fear is certain.

MARK TWAIN

(1835–1910)

You stand at the crossroads of the path of love and the
path of fear. Which do you choose to follow?

THE BUDDHA

(c.563–c.483BCE)

REVERSING NEGATIVE SELF-TALK

Self-talk is our internal dialogue – the words we use when we talk to ourselves, which reflect and create our emotional states. Negative self-talk is usually a mixture of half-truths and irrational thinking. Its consequences are to perpetuate negative emotions, such as pessimism, guilt, fear and anxiety.

Having a negative view of yourself is detrimental because it drastically limits your capabilities. While it is easy to spot when loved ones engage in negative self-talk, we often don't realize when we are doing this ourselves. You can begin to reverse your negative self-talk simply by developing awareness that you are doing it.

Often self-criticism does not reflect reality, but merely your interpretation of reality. If you believe your performance or qualities to be poor, consider whether you are being too hard on yourself. Look for the positive in your actions and achievements – this will help you keep things in perspective. Write down your negative thoughts and feelings and try to replace them with more positive thoughts, then write those down, too. Rather than attaching negative labels to yourself, such as "I'm stupid" or "I'm not good enough," instead say: "I'm an intelligent human being." Replace adjectives that give a catastrophic view of the world (such as "terrible", "awful" and "dreadful") for words that defuse the impact of a situation, such as "inconvenient" or "annoying". Relieve pressure on yourself by using phrases such as "I intend to" and "I would like to" instead of "must" and "have to". Avoid jumping to conclusions or assuming you know what someone else is thinking. Stop yourself if you start having thoughts such as: "There's no point in asking, she's bound to refuse."

The next time you catch yourself in negative self-talk, ask yourself: "What would I say to my best friend in this situation?" By imagining how we would help a friend, a compassionate, self-forgiving nature comes to the surface. When you make a mistake, continue to be supportive of yourself and remember that you deserve your love and patience. Allow your self-talk to be like the soothing, supportive words of a friend or mentor.

IMPROVE YOUR SELF-ESTEEM

Improving self-esteem takes effort, but the pay-off is
feeling good about yourself and your accomplishments.
Take a notebook and divide it up into sections, such as
"Things I've done that I feel proud of," "Things in life
that make me happy" and "What I like about myself
is …". Carry your notebook with you at all times,
and add to the sections whenever you have the
chance – aim to add three entries each day.

DISPEL JEALOUSY

Jealousy is one of the most destructive
emotions any human being can feel. Make a
conscious effort to catch it before it consumes you.
When someone achieves something you wish you could
have achieved, congratulate them on their success.
Try to feel happy for them, just as you would like
them to be happy for you if things were the other
way round. Aim to capitalize on feelings of jealousy
as an opportunity to examine where you want to be
in relation to where you are now. If necessary
redouble your efforts to help you
achieve your own life goals.

LIVING IN THE PRESENT

A well-known saying states that when one door closes, another one opens. However, many people spend so much time looking back at the closed door that they don't notice the new opportunities opening in front of them. Repeatedly dwelling on "if onlys" serves to anchor your thoughts firmly in the past. Similarly, fantasizing about the future and thinking about "what ifs" finds you living in the future. All too often we prevent ourselves from engaging with and fully enjoying the present.

Stress is often borne out of anxiety about the past – think how anxious you make yourself feel when you wish you had done or said something differently. The truth is, it is neither possible nor desirable to put back the clock – the past cannot be changed. Similarly we can never be certain of what lies ahead, so there's little point in worrying about the future. Start today to redirect your energy toward living for the moment. Within days you will see that by doing whatever comes naturally in the present, your future will be shaped by real experience.

A good way of tapping into this mindset is to imagine your life as a flowing river. Constantly referring to your past is like blasting cold air on the river so that it freezes. Each blast keeps the ice solid and unchanging. Imagine how stressful it is to be this solid! Now imagine that you turn away from your past, letting it go. Instead of constantly trying to recapture your past in the present, imagine the past nurtures you with the gentle, coaxing flow of experience. Learn to enjoy the movement of life's flow, without thinking about what has been left behind.

When looking forward remember that the river of life can flow round any obstacles. The course your future takes will depend on your actions in the here and now. Be mindful of every moment, savour every sensation and value every experience – in a moment they will be gone.

Mindfulness is a Zen meditation technique in which full focus is given to the present. Make a conscious effort to practise it. If you are chopping vegetables, empty your mind of everything else: focus on the act of chopping, the colours of the foods, their aromas. Love the sensation of being fully engaged with the world around you.

ACCEPTING CHANGE

Change is an inevitable part of life. However, for some of us change can be both upsetting and stressful – simply because we perceive that it takes away our sense of control. The only way to prevent change from causing stress is to let go of any desire to fight it, and look on it rather as an opportunity to enjoy new experiences and develop new skills and strengths. Keep in mind that human beings are among the most adaptable life forms on Earth. It is completely within you to adapt as life demands it, if you cultivate an attitude of acceptance.

Taoists talk of the principle of *wu wei* – or "non-doing". This does not mean that we literally do nothing, but rather that we avoid futile effort, allowing life to unfold in its own way. This is a good philosophy.

When change happens don't try to force it through quickly (as if the sooner it is over with, the sooner you will be back in control). Allow things to occur naturally. Try always to look for the positive in any change. If something bad happens accept it and let it go.

CREATE YOUR GOALS

Although constant focus on the future can be a source of anxiety, having a goal or goals in life – a master plan – is highly motivational and will give purpose to your present. This exercise will help you set yourself targets and prepare a life vision.

1 Sit comfortably. Close your eyes and spend five minutes thinking about the achievements you would like to have made in one month's, one year's, five years' and even ten years' time. Let your ideas flow naturally.

2 Take a pen and paper. Write down one goal you would like to achieve in each of the following categories: your family and relationships, career, health, and personal development. Beside each goal give yourself a time-frame for achieving it and note down the first three steps toward its fulfilment. Try to be realistic.

3 Check the list regularly to keep yourself on track. When you have made the first three steps, note down the next three, and so on, until you achieve each goal.

Chapter Four

relaxation for life

As we have seen from the previous two chapters, techniques to calm the body and mind abound. However, the final part of our journey should be to make relaxation an inherent part of our life, not simply something we do when the going gets tough. In this chapter we look at certain lifestyle strategies that can help to make harmful stress a thing of the past.

If you are in the peak of health, physically as well as mentally, you can cope more easily with anything life throws at you. Two of the changes we can make to our lifestyle are to adopt a healthy diet and to create a routine of regular exercise (which helps to burn off stress hormones and reset your body systems).

In addition we need to ensure that we have a healthy balance of work and homelife, and that neither one of these causes us undue stress. At work we need to develop a combination of good communication, organizational and time-management skills. To reap the true value of our homelife, we need to be able to switch off from the demands of our jobs, and find ways to nourish our close relationships.

Over the following pages you will find advice on how to eat healthily, exercise regularly, manage your workload and turn your home into an oasis of calm. Finally, we look at ways to improve a special relationship for a mutually supportive and relaxing life.

HEALTHY LIVING

Part of living a relaxed life is living a healthy life. All too often we take our health for granted until something starts to go wrong. By taking steps now to follow a healthy diet and lifestyle (such as doing regular exercise), you can pave the way for a future of optimum health and fitness, and deep contentment.

Many common illnesses, such as heart disease or high blood pressure, are linked with an unhealthy diet containing too much animal fat, salt, sugar and artificial additives, and not enough unrefined complex carbohydrates and fibre. The average adult needs to reduce fat intake by at least a quarter. Try to obtain beneficial fats from nuts, seeds, oily fish, and olive, rapeseed and walnut oils. Choose reduced-fat foods, and grill rather than fry. Fill up on unrefined, complex carbohydrates (found in wholegrain cereals, brown rice, wholemeal bread, wholewheat pasta and jacket potatoes).

Fruit and vegetables contain essential vitamins (A, B, C and E), as well as minerals, antioxidants and plant hormones. Eating at least five servings of fruit and vegetables per day reduces the risk of premature death from many illnesses, especially coronary heart disease. As it turns out, an apple a day *can* help keep the doctor away!

Drink plenty of water (at least six glasses a day) and try to maintain a healthy weight by ensuring that you do not exceed your calorie needs (approximately 2,000 a day for a woman; 2,500 for a man). If you smoke do your utmost to stop (many people find hypnosis helps, but check with your doctor first), and keep alcohol intake within the safe maximum of no more than two or three alcoholic drinks per day for men, one or two for women.

Of course, it's not just diet that keeps us healthy. Exercising regularly helps to burn off any build-up of stress hormones in the body and can reduce the risk of almost all serious illnesses. Try to exercise briskly for at least twenty to thirty minutes, two to three times per week. You could incorporate some exercise into your schedule by walking wherever and whenever possible. For example, try walking some of the way to work, or take the stairs instead of the elevator to reach your floor.

Tell me what you eat, and I will tell you what you are.

ANTHELME BRILLAT-SAVARIN

(1755–1826)

Food is the chief of all medicines.

THE UPANISHADS (c.800–c.400BCE)

AT ONE WITH NATURE

Nature has a wealth of antidotes to the stresses of modern living. We can delight in the variety provided by the changing seasons, and revel in nature's diversity. Getting in touch with nature should be one of your lifestyle strategies for relaxation.

The varying aspects of the natural world mean you can always find something in nature to match your mood. On the other hand, being at one with nature can influence your mood – and for the better. If you are feeling low, go for a walk in the fresh air, as this will often help to pick you up. This strategy is especially important if you suffer from seasonal affective disorder (a form of depression associated with lack of sunlight during the dark winter months). Even if it is raining outside, tell yourself that just as the warmth of spring inevitably follows the cold depths of winter, a happier mood can always follow feelings of sadness.

Get out into nature as often as you can. Take a walk in the forest, along a beach, in a place with a breathtaking view, or in some other location that is both inspiring and invigorating. As you are walking along, appreciate the beauty of your environment. Pick up leaves or rocks and examine them in detail – appreciate their combinations of shape, colour, texture and pattern.

Nature's gifts abound but not everyone can easily reach the wide open spaces of the countryside or shore. Furthermore, the convenience of artificial lighting, central heating and air conditioning means that we have become estranged from the cyclical rhythms of nature. However, you don't have to turn your back on the benefits of modern civilization in order to get back in touch with nature. Enjoy nature in your home simply by opening the windows to welcome the fresh air in. Cultivate tubs and flowerboxes on sills or balconies. Bring nature to you and at the same time enjoy the therapeutic effects of nurturing something and watching it grow and flourish. Select flowers for their delicate perfumes to delight your nose, as well as for their myriad, bright colours. As one poet suggests, we are "nearer God's heart in a garden than anywhere else on earth."

A WALK IN THE PARK

If you live in a city, walking in your local park will help you to reconnect with nature. Engage all your senses.

1 As you walk become aware of the texture of the ground beneath you. Is it springy or firm? Gravelly or smooth? Enjoy the breeze on your face. Reach down and touch the grass. Gently hold the head of a flower in your hands – feel how soft the petals are.

2 Enjoy the scents that perfume the air. Again, bend down to smell flowers. Smell the bark of a tree, and a fallen leaf. What can you hear? Try to detect minute sounds that often go unnoticed, such as the rustle of leaves, trickling water, chirping birds or the singing of crickets.

3 Explore the colours, shapes and visual depth of your surroundings. Look into the near, middle and far distance to appreciate the variety of the three-dimensional world. Try to distinguish separate leaves on the trees.

4 Practise this exercise at different times of the year to see how your senses detect changes from season to season.

Climb the mountains and get their good tidings.
Nature's peace will flow into you as sunshine flows into
trees. The winds will blow their freshness into you, and
the storms their energy, while cares will drop off
like falling leaves.

JOHN MUIR

(1838–1914)

I look at my world. Everything cooperates to bring me
life and strength. I look at the whole support system of
air and water, warmth and coolness, light and darkness
– everything contributes to my well-being.

ST IGNATIUS LOYOLA

(1491–1556)

MANAGING YOUR WORK

As much as work can be a source of fulfilment, it is often a source of anxiety and too often it eats into the precious time we have for relaxation. Time is a finite commodity and the more of it you spend on or at work, the less you have for fun. Good time-management and organizational skills are essential to help you maintain a balanced life that strikes a harmony between work and play.

At work start organizing your time by making a "to do" list. Write down all the things that need your attention and number the items in order of priority. Carry out the most important and pressing jobs first, before turning your attention to those that can wait. Part of prioritizing is to be assertive. Where necessary say "no" and mean it – don't agree to do more work than you know you can manage in the time available. Also, don't waste time dithering – decide what you need to do and get on with it. Learn how to pace yourself and work at a steady rate. Set yourself mini-goals (by this time I'll have done this, by that time I'll have done that). Keep a detailed (hour-by-hour) diary if it helps. Build in a little extra time to cope with meetings that overrun or unexpected calls. Above all, take regular breaks – a refreshed person is a more efficient person.

Prepare in advance for meetings. Make an agenda and stick to it. Reserve blocks of time for different activities, rather than jumping from job to job. Group essential telephone calls together and set a time limit in which to complete them. Deal swiftly with interruptions.

Delegate as much as possible. Appropriate delegation helps free up your own time and resources while still allowing you to retain some responsibility for a task. Those with good self-esteem usually make the best delegators: they don't mind relinquishing some control. Be sure to communicate effectively when you delegate; ask the person who is to do the task to repeat back what's expected. Be clear about where responsibility lies for each stage of the task.

Remember that above all your aim should be to "work to live", rather than "live to work" – never let your work become your life.

CALM COMMUTING

Being stuck in a car in traffic or delayed on public transport, and becoming anxious about arriving late to work, is one of the more stressful ways to start the day. In this situation the following exercise will help you restore a sense of calm. (If you are at the wheel, practise this only while you are stationary and it is safe to do so.)

1   Sit back comfortably, with your arms held loosely at your sides. Breathe in slowly and deeply, concentrating on the rise and fall of your abdomen. When you reach your full capacity for breathing in, immediately start to breathe out, emptying your lungs as much as possible.

2   Establish a rhythm by counting to 3 when breathing in and counting to 4 when breathing out. Breathe 5 complete breaths like this without pausing between breaths.

3   Practise this technique for rhythmic breathing as often as you need throughout your journey. Notice how much calmer you feel when you arrive for work.

WORK AND PLAY

Try to spend no more than two-thirds of your waking
day working, leaving the rest of your time for doing
things that help you relax. Be strict – set an alarm to
signal the end of your working day. When it goes off,
pack up your things in preparation for tomorrow and
then go to do something fun.

REWARD YOURSELF

Make a list of five simple activities that help you
relax. You might note down things such as a walk in
the park, a call to your best friend, reading today's
newspapers, mowing the lawn, listening to music and
going for a swim. Make a date with yourself to do one
of these things each day after work – they will soon
become an integral part of your life.

RELAXATION PROMPTS

Too many of us fail to leave worries behind in the work-place at the end of the day. Learning to switch off is a simply acquired but highly valuable skill.

Incorporating a short, regular routine at the end of your working day will help send a trigger to your brain that it's time for rest and relaxation. For example, you could spend a couple of minutes thinking about what you have achieved during the day – feel good about it! Write a "to do" list for the next day, then tidy your desk, turn off your computer and put your telephone on voicemail. You could also sit quietly (in the restroom, if it means you will be undisturbed) and do a simple five-minute relax-ation exercise. The exercise on page 47 or the one on page 50 would be perfect.

If a breathing technique does not appeal, try a visual-ization. Imagine your work time and home time occupy separate boxes. Visualize placing any work worries into the work box. Think about each worry in turn, then let it go as you put it away and visualize closing the box and pressing down the lid firmly. Tell yourself that once you have closed the lid of your work box, the worries that are stored there cannot overflow into the box of your home.

Once you have your thoughts organized, leave the office promptly. Avoid taking work documents with you, and make it a rule to turn off any mobile 'phones or bleepers when you get home.

Remember that the journey home can also act as a trigger for switching out of work mode. If you commute home on a bus or train, do something to draw your mind away from work: read a novel, newspaper or magazine. If you drive, listen to some music or a talking book.

If you work from home, try to dedicate one particular room to work. At the end of the day, tidy your desk and do a switching-off routine (as described opposite), then leave the room. Close the door firmly behind you and do not go back into the room until the following day.

Straight after work is a good time to build regular exercise into your life – the activity burns off any resid-ual stress hormones. Walk part of the way home or visit a gym or swimming pool.

MAKE YOUR ESCAPE

This visualization is intended to help you let go of your work worries. If you find it useful, you could try building it into your switching-off routine at the end of the day.

1 Sit comfortably, close your eyes and take a few slow, deep breaths. In your mind's eye visualize a brightly coloured hot-air balloon anchored to the ground.

2 The balloon seems inviting – a great way to escape the pressures of the day. It sways gently in the breeze. Imagine that you climb into the wicker basket.

3 You look down, trying to work out how to take off and you see that the basket is weighed down by stones – these stones represent your workday problems.

4 You heave the stones over the side, one by one. The basket soon starts to wobble and before long the balloon begins to drift upward. High up in the sky you feel free – spend a few moments imagining that you navigate in the gentle breeze under a warm, welcoming sun.

CREATING A SANCTUARY

Home should be somewhere safe and secure, a peaceful place in which we can retreat from the pressures of the outside world. Living in a simple, uncluttered environment is one of the best ways of making tranquillity part of your everyday life.

Feng shui (meaning "wind" and "water") is the Chinese art of arranging your living spaces according to the forces of the universe. In feng shui the energy patterns acting on your home are considered some of the most important influences on your life and may be used to create a harmonious, protective place for relaxation, good health and prosperity.

As a first step to harmonizing your living space, ensure that you are clear about the purpose of each room and what activity should take place there. Try to create an atmosphere appropriate to each room's function. For example, the bedroom should be a calm, tranquil place designed for sleep and intimacy. Try to avoid using the bedroom for any other purpose, such as work. If turning part of your bedroom into a work area is unavoidable, partition off the working space with a screen. This will help segregate the tranquil energy associated with sleep from the active energy of work.

Natural daylight has a refreshing yet soothing effect on your well-being. Where possible let sunshine into your home – perhaps filtered through fine muslin curtains to impart a softer, more relaxing feel. Table lights and wall uplighters work to create a softer mood for the evening (especially when fitted with dimmer switches) by providing several light sources instead of just one overhead beam.

When making your home a sanctuary, think about replicating nature using the earth's palette of restful greens, creams and beiges offset by rich yet subtle shades of terracotta, ochre or cinnamon. Natural textiles, such as linen, cotton and hessian, as well as wood or stone finishes, will complete the natural look.

Small, individual features, such as cushions or sofa throws, plants and decorative items, enable you to personalize a space with favourite colours and patterns.

SHADES OF RELAXATION

In feng shui different colours are believed
to have different properties. Blue is a restful shade,
but should not be used to excess in a room – especially
dark blue, which absorbs and stores energy in an
unpredictable way. Creams, off-whites and beiges are
suitable for any room. Light greens are good for the
bathroom and sitting room. Yellows and strong earth
colours work well in the kitchen, and soft, warm peach
or pink tones are soothing for the bedroom. Strong
reds and oranges are considered rather overpowering
and therefore unsuitable for use in the home.

FINDING TRANQUILLITY TOGETHER

Even the most successful relationships can sometimes be a source of anxiety. However, close relationships, based on respect, trust, good communication, kindness and empathy, are highly rewarding and worth nurturing.

Ensure that you spend quality time with your partner. Prioritize your relationship over your work – your loved ones will be there long after the office door has closed. Make time to do lots of enjoyable and relaxing things together. Go for walks and picnics, visit exhibitions at local museums and art galleries. Build up your shared experiences: do a windsurfing course together, learn a language, learn to ski and so on.

Make relaxation a mutual treat – have a candlelit bath together, meditate together or go for a run together.

Try to use your holiday time wisely – rather than taking a whole week off, it may sometimes be more beneficial to take off just a day or two so you can spend a long weekend in each other's company. Use this quality time to revitalize and strengthen your relationship.

Inevitably relationships undergo periods of change and even disagreement. At difficult times express yourself calmly and honestly. Be assertive but not aggressive and set your priorities clearly. Listen as well as talk, and don't interrupt one another. Be forgiving – remember that none of us is perfect. Give each other the space to get things wrong from time to time. Express your opinions and beliefs and be honest and open if you don't understand something your partner is saying. Always be yourself and remember that you have the right to be respected – just as your partner must be respected, too.

A common complaint of warring partners is that old grievances surface every time they have a row. Make a promise to one another to communicate openly at all times and to resolve things as they arise. Once they are resolved let them go and don't bring them up again unless it is relevant to do so. During a discussion always stick to the point. If you are upset about something in particular, make a statement about it to your partner. Tell them what the problem is and how it makes you feel. Be concise, then give them the chance to explain.

The moment you have in your heart this extraordinary
thing called love and feel the depth, the
delight, the ecstasy of it, you will discover that
for you the world is transformed.

JIDDU KRISHNAMURTI

(1895–1986)

This is the miracle that happens every time
to those who really love; the more they give,
the more they possess.

RAINER MARIA RILKE

(1875–1926)